LATERAL
LOGICAL MAZES
for the Serious Puzzler

LARRY EVANS

Sterling Publishing Co., Inc.   New York

Library of Congress Cataloging-in-Publication Data Available

10 9 8 7 6 5 4 3

Published by Sterling Publishing Company, Inc.
387 Park Avenue South, New York, N.Y. 10016
© 1996 by Larry Evans
Distributed in Canada by Sterling Publishing
c/o Canadian Manda Group, One Atlantic Avenue, Suite 105
Toronto, Ontario, Canada M6K 3E7
Distributed in Great Britain and Europe by Cassell PLC
Wellington House, 125 Strand, London WC2R 0BB, England
Distributed in Australia by Capricorn Link (Australia) Pty Ltd.
P.O. Box 6651, Baulkham Hills, Business Centre, NSW 2153, Australia
Manufactured in the United States of America

Sterling ISBN 0-8069-6116-3

CONTENTS

Introduction   4

Doors and Stairs   9

Solid Geometry   17

Letters and Words   25

Math and Logic   31

Geometry   37

Follow the Arrows   43

Mixed Bag   49

Solutions   55

Index   64

INTRODUCTION

Many, many years ago, in a far off galaxy, I created a variety of labyrinths called "3-Dimensional Mazes." I was very happy with my invention and published several books and posters over the next few years. All was right and proper in the galaxy.

But, time marched on, and I felt some slight qualms of concern over my invention. The images of the mazes were still interesting, but the puzzles themselves were not as challenging as I wanted. After all, a maze is always solvable—you just fill up all the pathways and eventually you will prevail. That exercise can be fun, but what if a new wrinkle were added to the challenge?

Lateral Logic Mazes is that new wrinkle. You are invited to open doors, change the direction of arrows, connect the sides of solid objects, and follow paths etched on glass. Each puzzle in this book has an extra element added to push past the threshold of the maze experience. See if you can solve them without looking at the solutions in the back of the book.

Lateral Logic Maze 1 is a trick puzzle to start you on your way. Read the instructions very carefully. Hint: The word "enter" figures prominently in this puzzle.

1: THE INS AND OUTS

Begin your trip to the pyramids at the upper diamond. You must enter each pyramid and diamond only once. Exit at the lower diamond.

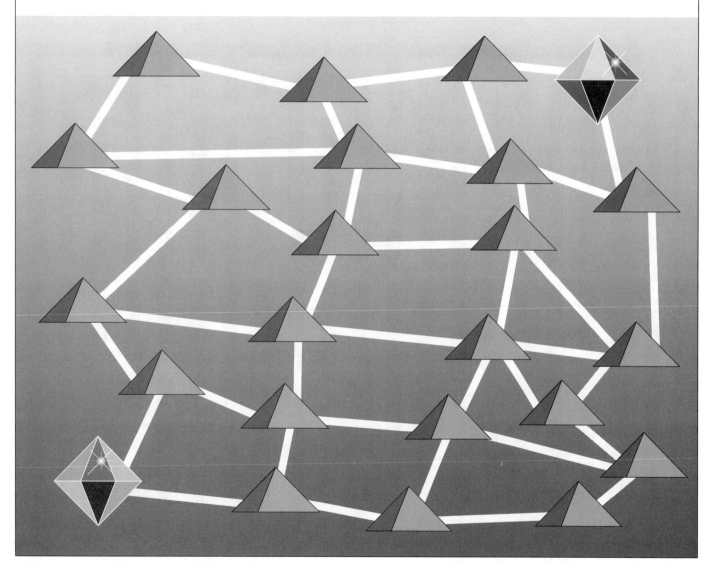

2: ROUND ABOUT

Begin at the IN arrow and follow the arrows to the OUT arrow. You must touch all six arrows within the maze, and you must also follow each arrow's direction when you reach it. The path travels over and under itself. You may only touch each arrow once, but you may take each path as often as you like.

3: THE BARRICADES

Begin at the IN arrow and remove only TWO barricades to solve the maze.

4: ALMOST STRAIGHT DOWN

Enter the maze at any point at the top and follow the black path to the bottom exit. Many paths lead to the exit; however, you may travel upwards only ONCE.

5: IN THE BEGINNING

Begin with the triangle, visit every black circle only once, and then return to the triangle.

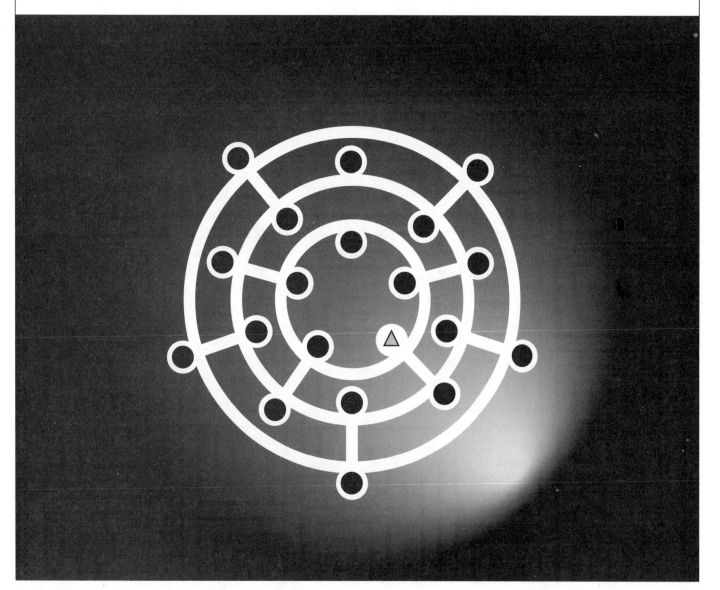

DOORS AND STAIRS

Now that you've had a tiny hint of what a Lateral Logic Maze is, let's move on to the next plateau. The next seven puzzles ask you to project yourself into the maze and deal with open and closed doors, stairways, upside-down rooms and walls without doors at all.

In Maze 6, you enter the building through the front door and proceed into each room in a logical fashion. Maze 7 takes you on a bit longer trip through a building, and Maze 8 gives you three stories of an office building. Be very careful when you climb the stairs in Maze 8 because you don't want to get lost.

Good luck on your travels in this section. We'll meet again when you reach Solid Geometry.

6: ONE TO WIN

Enter the maze and walk through ALL the open doors while opening only ONE closed door. You may pass through each opening only once.

7: THE HOUSE OF MYSTERY

In this mystery-house maze, open only FIVE doors on your way from the IN arrow to the OUT arrow.

8: THE OFFICE BUILDING

Enter the three-story office building at the main entrance and exit at the same place. You must visit all three floors using the stairs. You may only open TWO doors during your visit. Be sure to use the correct stairs!

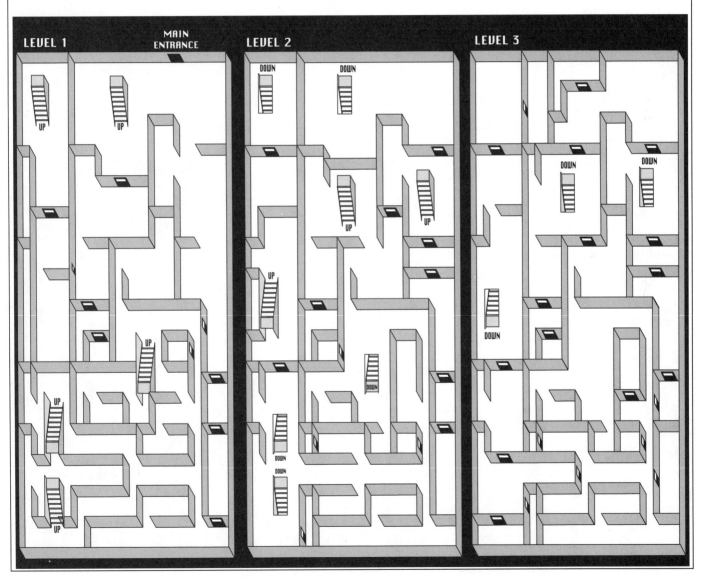

9: WALLS ONLY

Begin at the IN arrow and enter each enclosed room only once, then exit. How many doors must you cut?

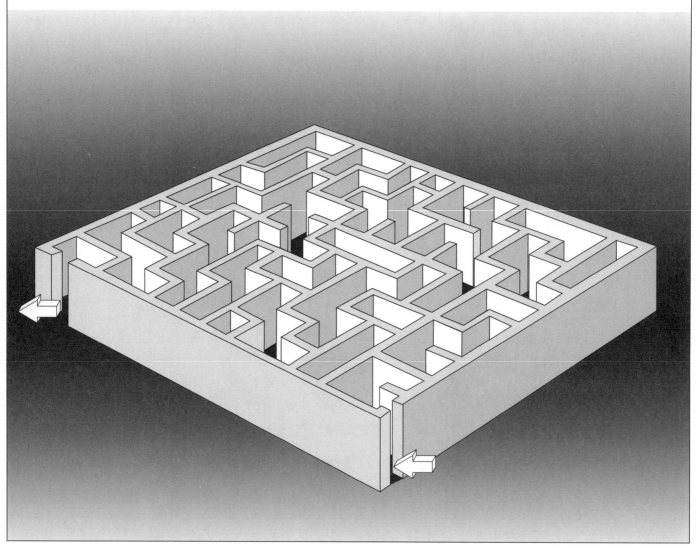

10: THE WAREHOUSE

Enter the warehouse and walk to the back exit. You may open only FIVE doors on your journey.

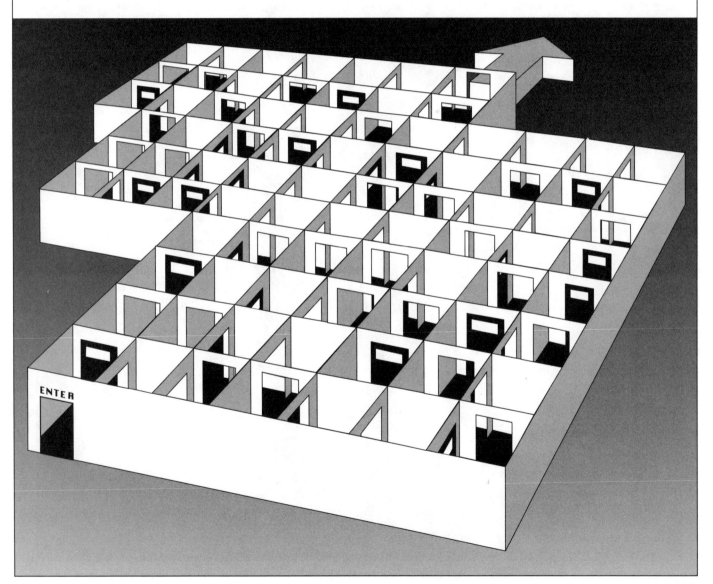

11: DOWN SIDE UP

Travel to the central core from the IN arrow. Once there, jump to the center of the upside-down maze and find your way out.

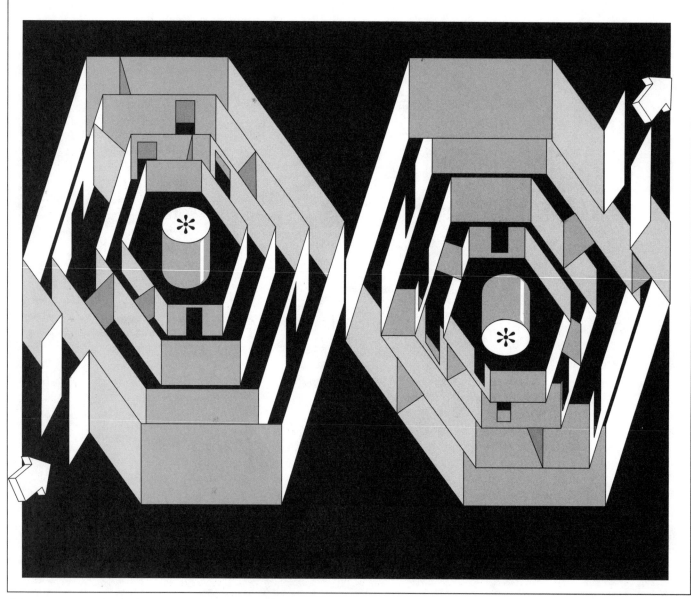

12: UNDER CONSTRUCTION

Enter the unfinished high-rise building at the marked elevator. Take the elevator to any floor that has an elevator door. Use the elevators and stairways to reach the exit. You may use each bank of elevators only once, and you may cross over from floor to floor only on the construction bridges. You may build one new stairway if you need it.

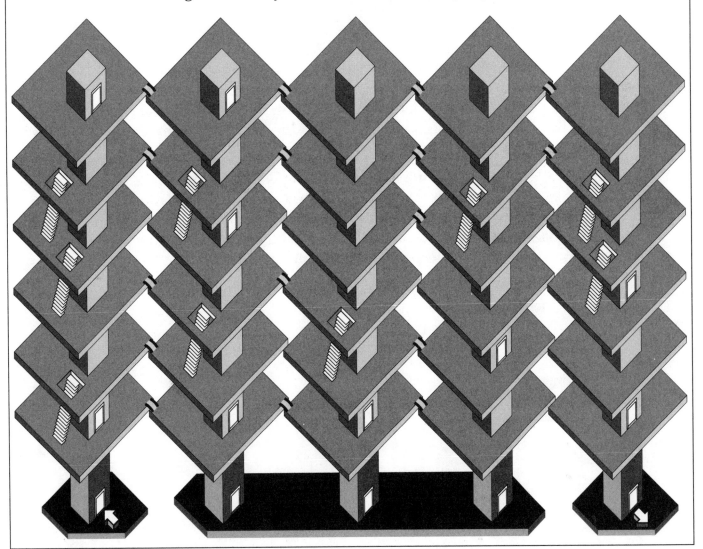

SOLID GEOMETRY

This section deals with the visual aspects of three-dimensional objects viewed either as though they are clear glass or as solids, some of which have been taken apart and left scattered about. Even though you can see all the sides of a pyramid, for instance, deciding just where the path travels can be a bit tricky.

The secret of three-dimensional maze solving is to try to visualize the object as you might see it from a point other than the one the illustration forces upon you. Maze 16, Folding Fools, is a good example of a simple maze that has been complicated by folding it in half. Now you have to look at the puzzle from two separate directions.

As you breeze through this section, remember: "There is a logical way to solve these puzzles."

See you later at Words and Letters.

13: CLEAR LOGIC

Follow the path from the IN arrow to the OUT arrow. The path is etched on clear glass so you can follow it around the solid shape. The path flows over and under itself.

14: BOXED IN

All six sides of a box are shown here. To solve the maze, you must visualize the paths as printed on clear glass. Then fit the left box over the right so that the paths line up. The paths go over and under each other.

15: CUBE ROOT

Here are the six sides of a cube. A maze pathway beginning and ending at the ball wraps over and under itself as it traverses the cube. Find your way from start to finish to solve the puzzle.

16: FOLDING FOOLS

This maze is printed on a piece of paper that has been folded in half.
Trace the paths as they go over and under each other.

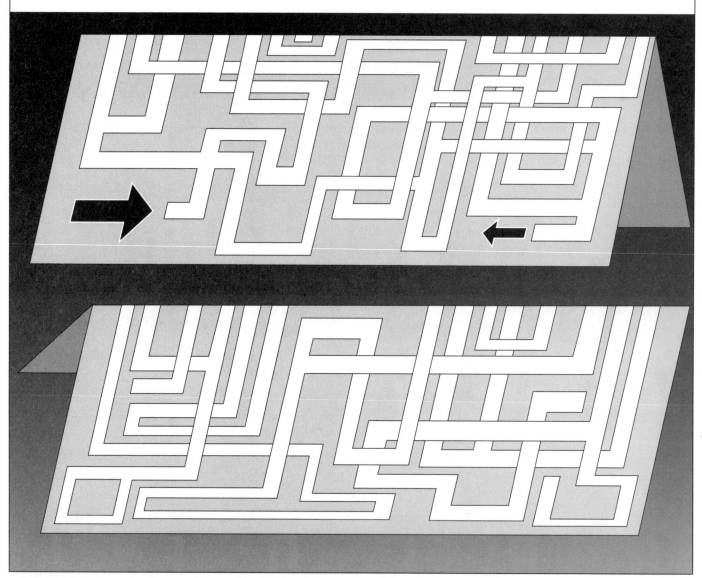

17: THE PYRAMID

You can see all five sides of a pyramid here. Find the IN arrow and work your way around the sides and bottom to the OUT arrow.

18: MÖBIUS MADNESS

The sketch shows the completed Möbius strip with both the IN and OUT arrows. Using the sketch as a guide, trace the path on the unattached strips. Try to do this puzzle without building the Möbius strip.

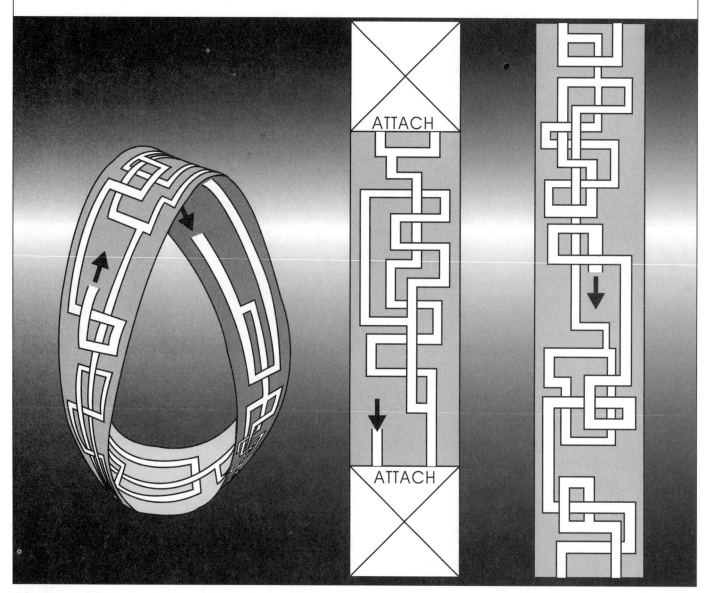

19: THREE CUBES

When three cubes are placed next to each other, fourteen sides are visible (including the bottom). All fourteen sides are illustrated here (three sides are shown twice). Trace the path from IN to OUT as the trail crosses over and under itself and moves from cube to cube.

LETTERS AND WORDS

Congratulations! You've made it into the valley of lost letters. If you've ever used words, you will just love this section.

You will journey from Alphatrek to Cat and Mouse on this voyage. Get out your dictionary (just kidding) and make sure all the letters are in there because in these puzzles, letters have an elusive quality and tend to have an attitude.

Remember, if you must give up, the solutions are in the back of the book.

See you when you reach Math and Logic.

20: ALPHATREK

Begin at letter **A** and visit each letter only once, staying on the paths. Once you reach a letter within a circle, you may leave that circle on any path available. The paths cross over and under each other.

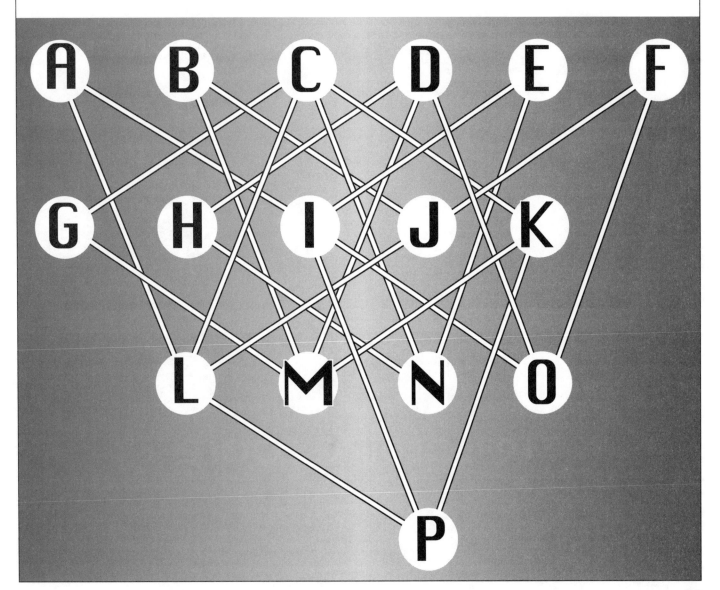

21: YOU'RE LOGICAL?

Starting with the letter Y, touch all the lettered squares only once to spell an obvious sentence. The paths cross over and under each other.

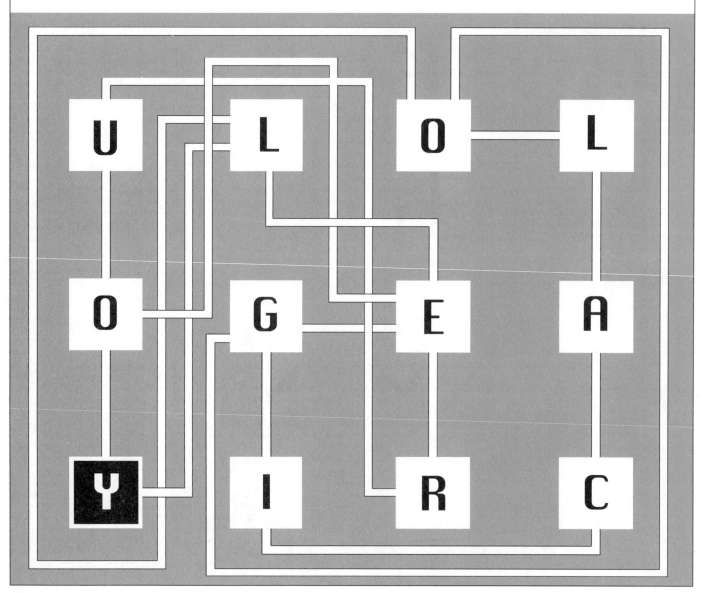

22: ABRACADABRA

Connect pairs of the same letters (A and A, B and B, etc.) without crossing a path created by connecting other pairs. Stay on the white line.

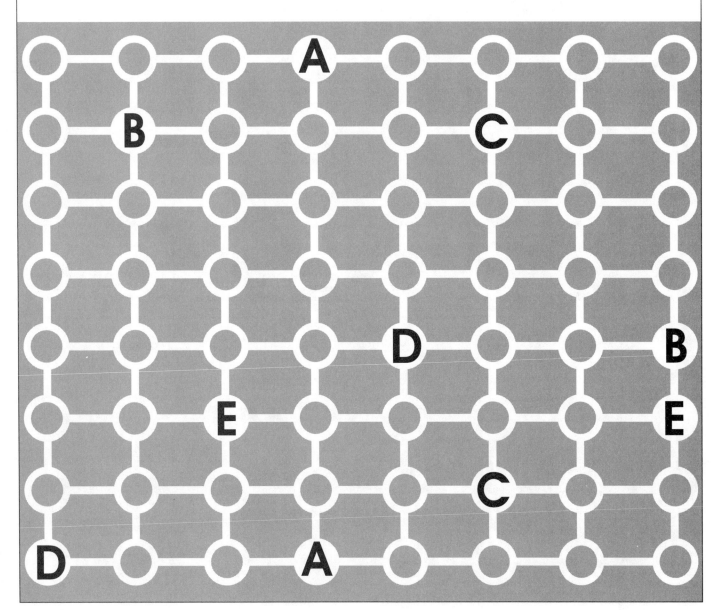

23: ALPHABET ZOOP

Beginning with the letter **A** trace a path to the letter **Z**. When you reach the end of the alphabet, begin again with an adjacent **A**. You may travel horizontally and vertically, forward and backwards, but not diagonally. One letter is incorrect. Change it to solve the puzzle.

A	B	C	D	E	F	G	H	I	J	K	L	M	N	O	P	Q	R
B	C	D	E	F	G	H	I	J	K	L	M	P	Q	R	S	T	U
C	D	I	H	G	J	I	P	O	N	M	N	O	X	W	T	W	U
D	E	J	K	L	K	P	Q	G	A	G	F	E	D	C	U	U	X	A
E	F	M	L	M	N	O	R	S	H	I	J	A	B	A	Z	Y	B
F	G	R	S	T	I	D	C	T	I	L	K	H	I	J	G	F	E
A	H	Q	A	U	H	F	B	U	J	M	N	M	L	K	H	I	J
J	I	P	O	U	G	E	A	V	K	P	O	F	M	N	O	P	Q
K	L	M	N	W	X	Y	Z	W	L	Q	R	E	O	O	P	Q	R
B	A	Z	Y	X	A	X	Y	X	U	T	S	O	P	Q	R	A	S
C	D	K	J	I	A	Y	Z	A	B	C	B	C	F	G	S	U	T
F	E	L	A	H	G	F	E	D	C	Z	C	D	E	H	T	U	U
G	H	M	N	O	P	U	V	W	X	Y	B	K	J	I	U	W	Y
I	J	K	L	M	Q	T	N	O	M	Z	A	L	M	N	O	X	Y
R	Q	P	O	N	R	S	P	Q	R	S	T	U	V	W	X	Y	Z

24: CAT AND MOUSE

To help the cat find the mouse, begin with the word "CAT" and work through the maze to "MOUSE," traveling in any direction (horizontally, vertically, diagonally, forward, and backwards) spelling words of three letters or more. When you reach the end of a word, begin a new word with an adjacent letter.

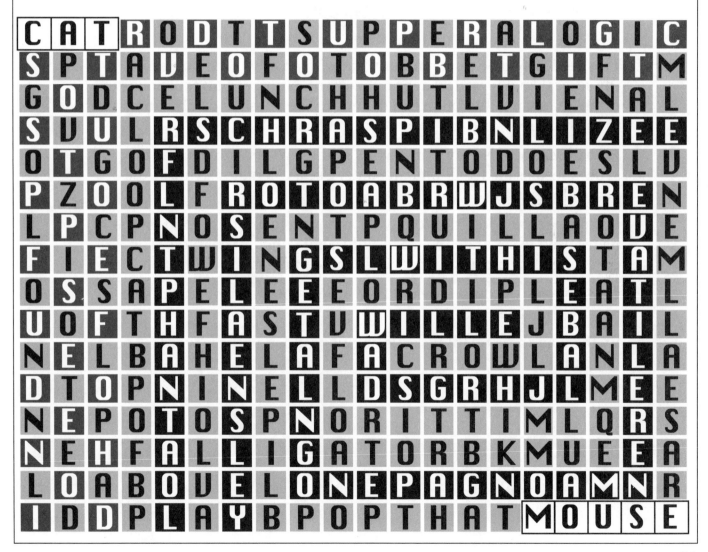

MATH AND LOGIC

This section will be a snap for anyone with an advanced degree in linear, logical, mathematical aggrandizement. Number Fun took longer to create than any other puzzle in the book. The possible combinations are in the hundreds, and it's hard not to get lost.

Pinball Madness is more fun if you zip through the numbers at the same speed as an actual pinball game. Use a calculator to hurry the game along.

It is probably a good idea to pay no attention to anything said on these pages used to separate the mazes into semi-coherent chapters. The odds of getting a clue or hint within these paragraphs are next to nil.

These mazes, of course, are not the hardest ones. Just wait until you reach Geometry!

By the way, there might be hints or clues hidden in these words. Could happen!

25: NUMBER FUN

Start with the number **3**, in the center of this maze and travel 3 spaces horizontally or vertically. Then move the number of spaces indicated on the NEW square. Work your way to any of the squares marked with a symbol. You may travel over each square as often as you like.

❄	8	6	5	7	7	2	4	6	2	❄
8	3	9	6	3	8	3	9	5	6	4
4	9	5	3	6	9	9	4	6	8	9
6	8	3	9	7	3	4	4	2	5	4
2	5	8	3	4	9	3	2	3	9	1
4	2	4	6	9	**3**	5	8	3	9	2
9	5	6	2	6	7	9	2	6	8	2
6	3	8	4	7	4	8	4	9	9	6
5	8	5	4	4	7	5	9	4	8	4
2	7	4	2	5	7	2	9	2	8	6
❄	4	9	4	4	2	7	5	3	1	❄

26: WIN SUM—LOSE SUM

Begin at **2** and move in any direction (including diagonally) to an adjacent square. Add the number in this square to that in the square you just left. The sum of those two numbers will be a number in an adjacent square (2 + 4 = 6, etc.). Move there. Repeat this process until you reach **100**.

2	4	6	5	11	6	17	10	49	2	51	4	89	4	93	7	100
6	2	5	13	2	19	2	1	27	10	37	0	37	2	8	95	6
8	3	11	2	15	1	48	5	0	27	1	28	51	1	87	5	90
2	1	3	15	5	20	2	22	4	26	30	2	3	38	6	90	6
10	7	9	2	11	9	46	1	45	3	3	30	54	2	81	3	84
6	16	5	12	1	53	1	54	32	3	29	5	6	40	5	85	3
16	6	21	9	12	30	6	8	5	6	42	35	60	1	76	9	81
4	2	24	4	21	3	24	47	37	1	38	3	41	0	41	0	5
20	0	18	28	25	7	15	5	41	4	4	38	6	44	60	2	76
3	18	9	8	2	10	5	42	0	43	42	44	1	43	1	42	1
23	28	2	26	25	6	40	2	41	0	6	2	56	6	61	10	75
6	2	4	1	0	29	2	31	4	42	50	46	10	6	53	2	78
29	30	25	2	26	4	38	0	37	56	1	6	67	2	73	6	2
0	1	6	7	0	3	4	39	1	0	56	43	2	46	2	47	76
29	31	0	31	29	6	34	2	36	56	6	62	69	2	71	9	4
1	32	3	4	7	4	1	9	0	49	62	8	70	2	72	0	72
30	2	4	35	2	37	33	43	5	49	0	54	0	9	71	0	71
37	1	36	4	40	2	39	4	43	6	49	5	54	9	63	10	73

27: PINBALL MADNESS

Begin at the pinball and follow the lines as they bounce off the walls and the numbers. When you reach a number ball, you may take any path that leads out of that ball. Reach a score of 100 and return to the pinball without adding any more points. You may take any path as often as you like.

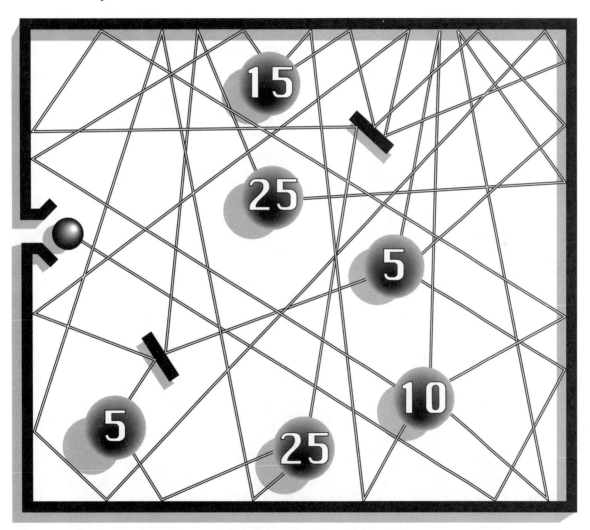

28: MORE PINBALL MADNESS

Again, begin at the pinball and follow the lines as they cross over each other until they bounce off the walls or hit the orbs containing the fractions. When you reach a number ball, you may take any path that leads out of that ball. Reach a score of 5 and return to the pinball without adding any more points. You may take any path as often as you like.

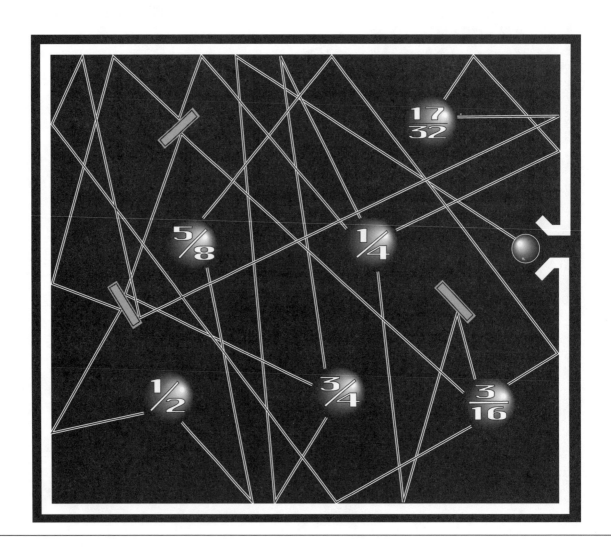

29: PAST PRESIDENTS

Each president has his twin brother with him today. Find the fastest route from President 1 to President 12, touching each president and his twin only once.

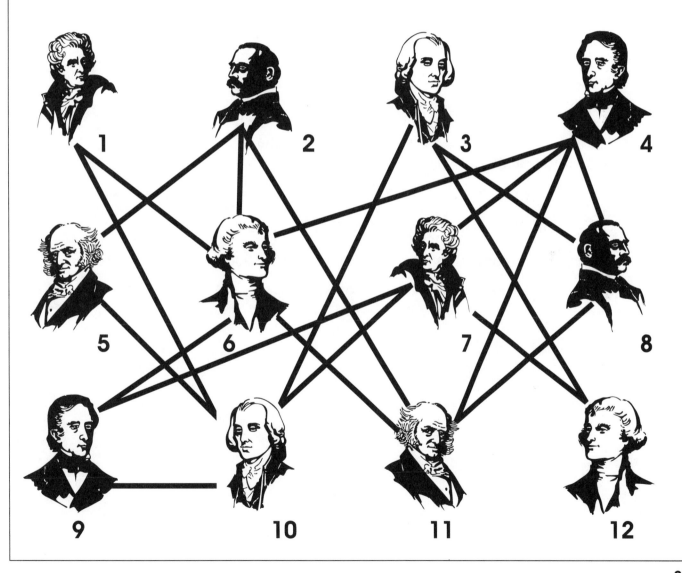

GEOMETRY

Simple geometric shapes: hexagons, squares, triangles, and hex-nuts! Easy stuff for those geo-types. But these Lateral Logic Mazes add just a touch of madness to the proceedings. Maybe it's a hex or maybe it's a square. Or maybe someone's put a hex on a square. It's obviously a triangle, but where did the extra piece come from?

Don't be intimidated by a circle that has to become a square or things like that. Before you challenge each circle to a duel, try the maze as it is and see where it takes you. You might be surprised.

Once you overcome these puzzles, the rest of the book will be a breeze.

We'll see you next at Follow the Arrows.

30: HEX OR SQUARE

The pieces below fit together as either a square or a hexagon. Make your decision and build one of the options. Now solve the maze as the path winds over and under itself.

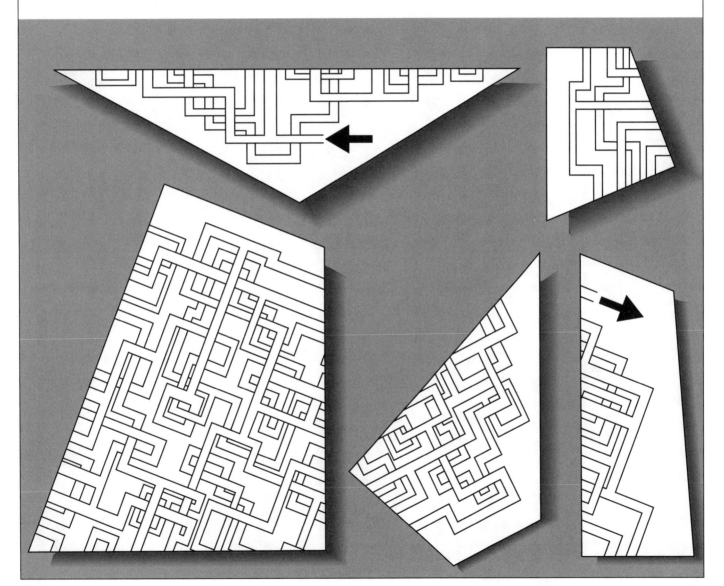

31: THE RED HERRING

Four of the triangles below form a larger triangle. The path on the small triangles weaves over and under itself from start to finish. There are no dead ends. However, one of the triangles is a red herring and does not work with the others to complete the maze. First, put the proper triangles together, then, complete the maze.

32: SQUARE CIRCLES

Begin with the **S** and work your way through the maze horizontally and vertically (NOT diagonally), alternating from square to circle. Try to reach the **C**. By the way, one circle should be a square. Change it to win.

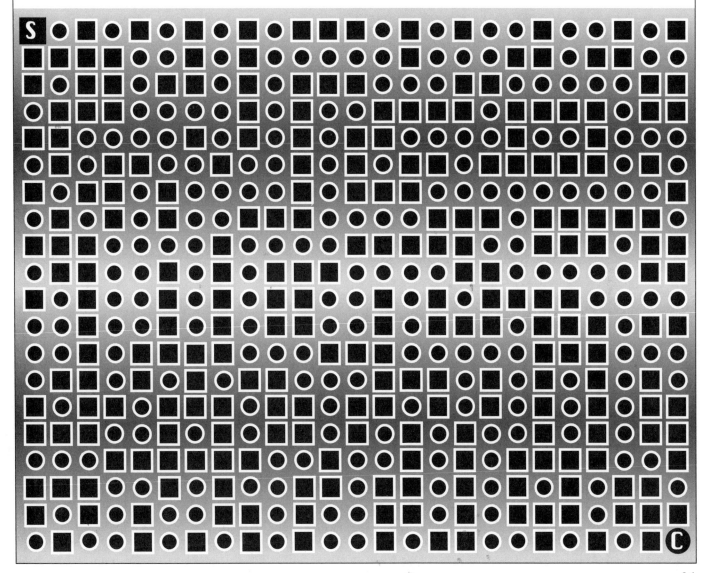

33: THREE NUTS

The path shown on the puzzle begins at the **1**, and touches all the nuts only once. Find a path that begins at **2** and also touches all the nuts. Now find another that begins at **3**. It's not as easy as it looks.

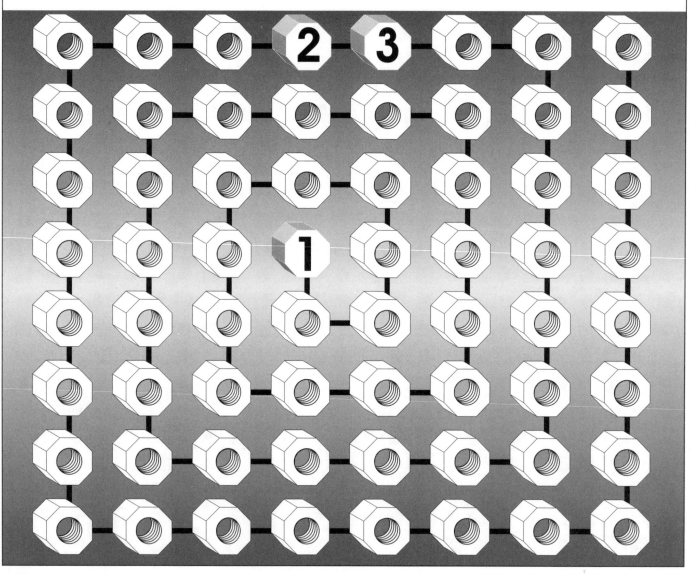

34: ROUND AND ROUND

If you start from the central globe, only one of the four mazes leads to an OUT arrow. Using just your eyes, can you discover the correct maze?

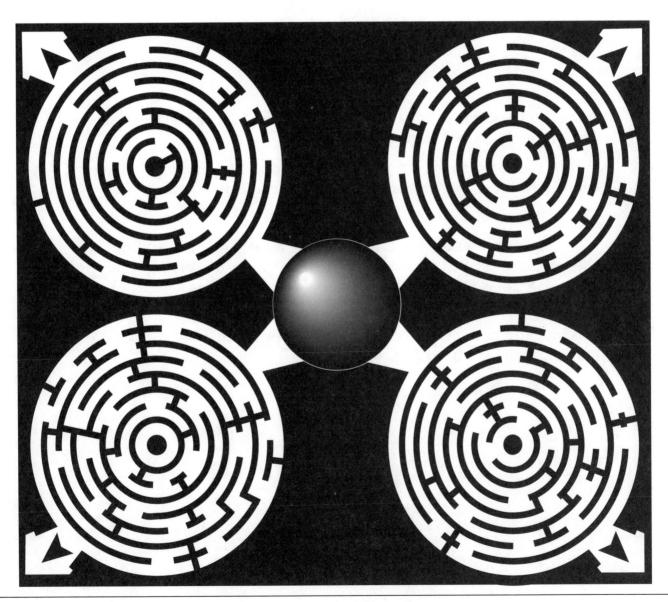

FOLLOW THE ARROWS

You've made it through the hard stuff (trust me). Now you can just float through the rest of the book.

Follow the Arrows is a piece of cake. What could be simpler? You just enter the maze, go where the arrows point, and exit the maze.

OK, so it's not that easy.

A few of the arrows do point in the wrong direction, but you should be able to find those bad arrows fast. The secret to easily solving "bad arrow" mazes is to look first at what the real problem is (Maze 36) and deal with what the puzzle asks you to do.

Or move to a new city and change your name. Then, head on over to the final chapter, Mixed Bag.

35: ENDING WELL

Follow the arrows and touch every space except the center. Be careful, however. Two arrows are facing in the WRONG direction.

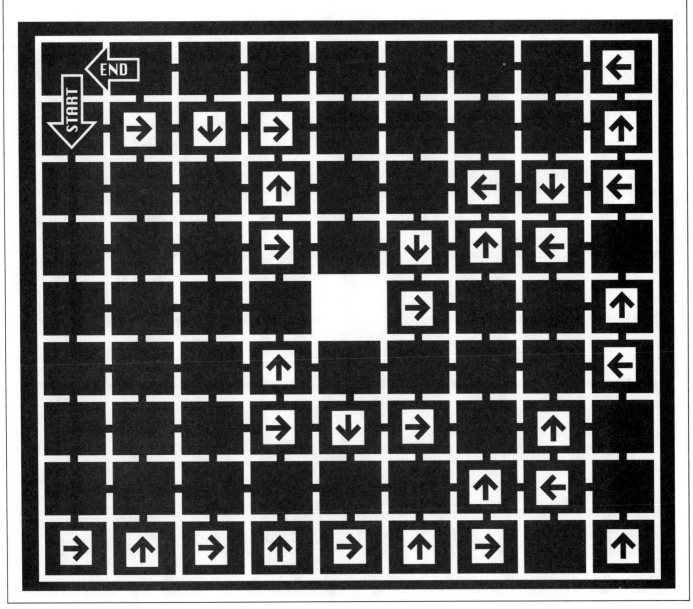

36: GONE BUT NOT FORGOTTEN

Follow the arrows to return to the start, touching every white space only once. Warning: there are three arrows missing.

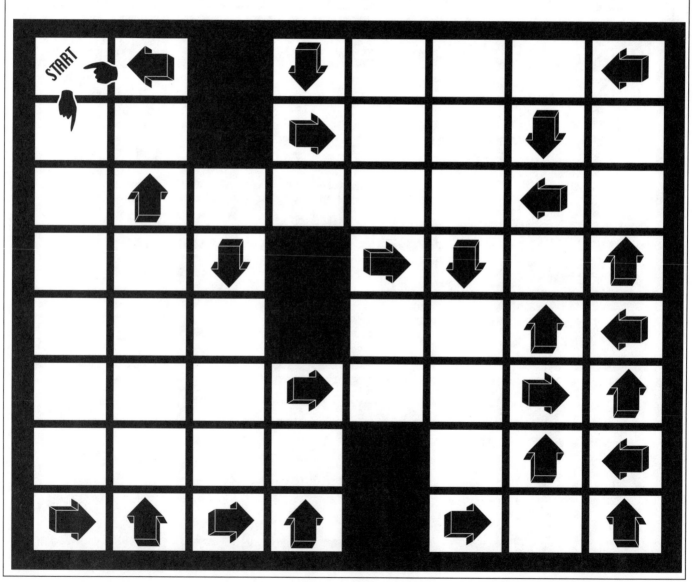

37: THE BAD ARROW

Follow the arrows from the IN arrow to the OUT arrow. The only problem here is that ALL the black arrows are pointing in the opposite direction—except ONE.

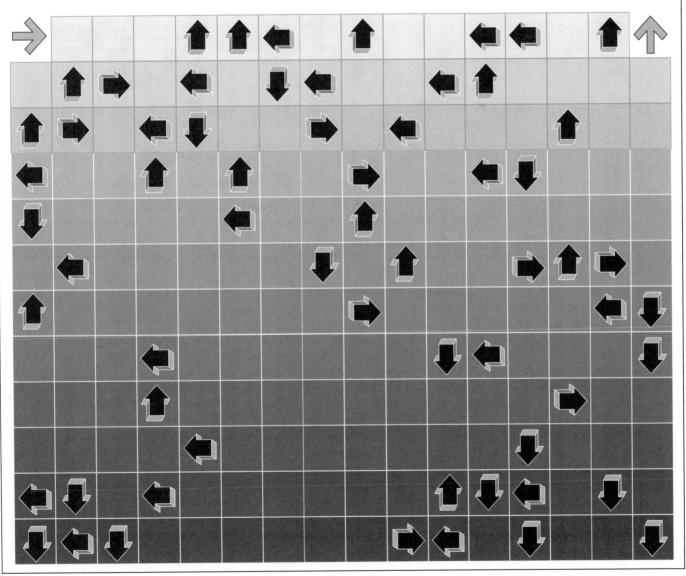

38: BLACK AND WHITE

Enter the maze and follow the arrows to the OUT arrow. In this maze all
the white arrows (except one) are facing in the opposite direction, and
all the black arrows (except one) are facing the correct direction.

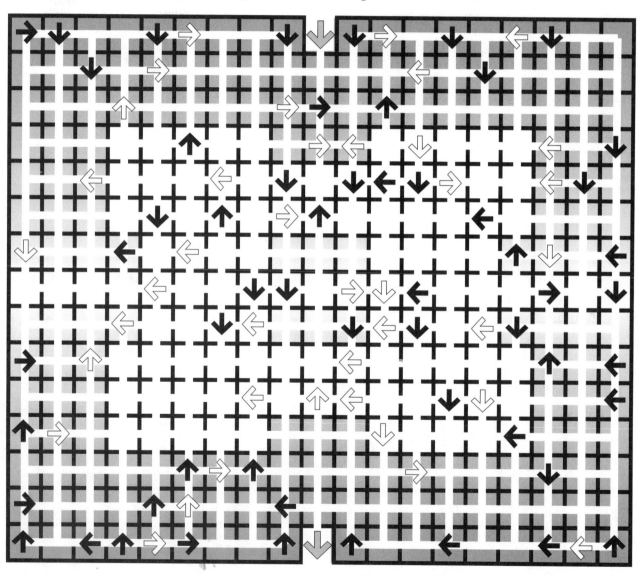

39: ARROW CUBES

Start your trip at ball **A** and follow the arrows. You must visit five of the six globes and leave the maze at ball **B**. When you reach a globe, you may take any exit available. When you reach a double arrow, you may travel in either direction indicated. By the way, one arrow is facing the wrong way (not a double arrow).

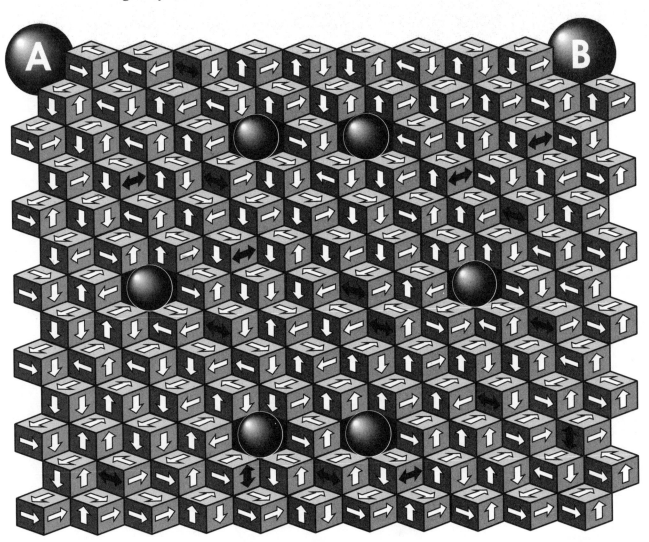

MIXED BAG

Well here you are. You've made it to the final rung of Lateral Logic Mazes. By solving all the earlier mazes, without ever looking at the answers, you have established yourself as a Master Mazemeister.

As a reward, I've engineered the final puzzles to look hard, although they are really easy. You've earned it.

As long as you're here, why not just give these next puzzles a go? Then you will have scored a perfect one hundred percent.

See you when you've finished for an almost final word.

40: BUILDING BRIDGES

Can you travel from Duringham to Bellabora, building only FOUR
bridges over the river delta? What is the LARGEST number of bridges
you could build without retracing your path and still arrive at
Bellabora? You may return to START as often as you can.

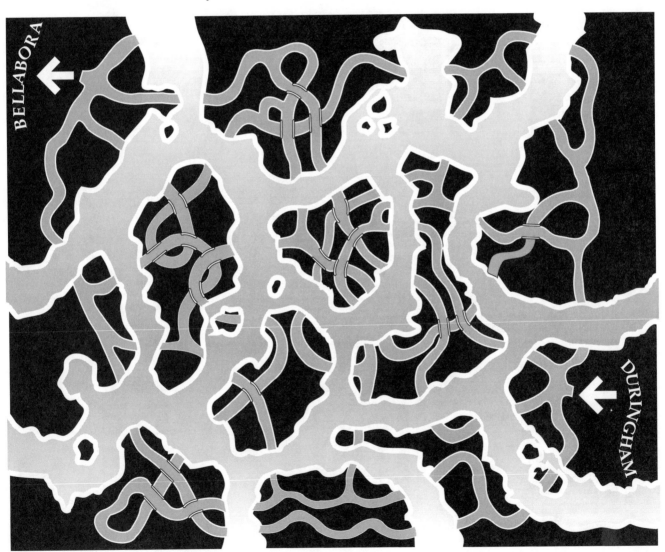

41: JIGSAW MAZE

These jigsaw pieces have a maze path inscribed on them. I have rearranged the pieces, but not rotated them. Find the path between the IN arrow and the OUT arrow. The path travels over and under itself.

42: JIGSAW TOO

Put the pieces together and follow the path from orb to orb. The paths go over and under each other. They are also turned sideways and upside down. By the way, there is one piece too many.

43: CANNONBALLS

Enter the maze and visit exactly one hundred cannonballs before exiting. Don't just count the balls you see, count the entire stack. Hint: you don't have to visit ALL the cannonball stacks.

44: MONEYBAGS

Beginning at any corner money bag, travel to as many bags as you like and collect the money indicated on that bag. However, you may NOT collect any money from a bag lying on the same line as a bag you have previously selected. Try to collect $77.00.

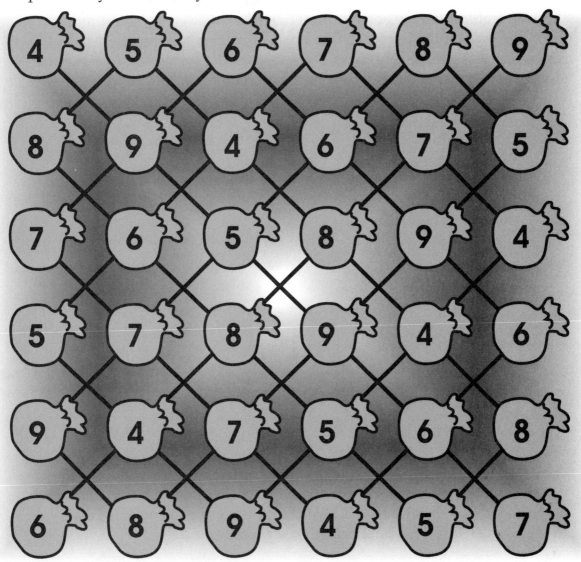

THE SOLUTIONS

You have reached this page either because you have solved all the puzzles or because you feel that just a peek at the solutions might help to do so. Or maybe you like to read books backwards.

If you are tempted to check out the solutions first, let me warn you. Bolts of lightning have been known to strike those who would meddle with the laws of the universe. The rules of puzzle solving are strict and unyielding. All those who would glance into the forbidden fruits of the solution section are banished from the land of Truth and Boldness forever.

Of course, if you're just browsing...

The maze illustration used throughout this book is known as the Chartres Cathedral Labyrinth and was visited by this author on one of his many jaunts into the nice weather.

SOLUTIONS

Maze 1

You must enter the first pyramid and return to the diamond to solve the puzzle.

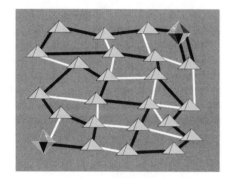

Maze 3

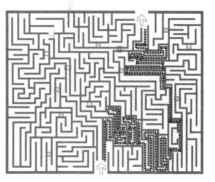

Maze 6

Maze 4

Maze 7

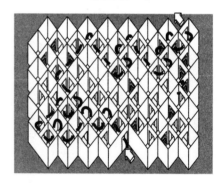

Maze 2

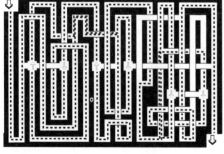

Maze 5

SOLUTIONS

Maze 8

You must use the same stairs and door going up as going down.

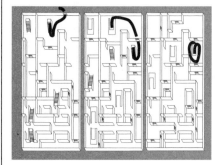

Maze 9

26 Doors.

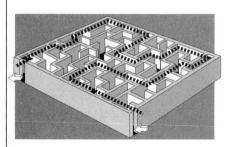

Maze 10

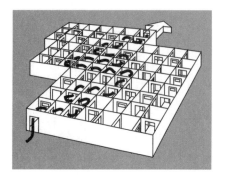

Maze 11

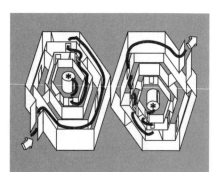

Maze 12

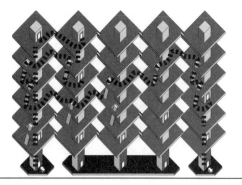

Maze 13

Maze 14

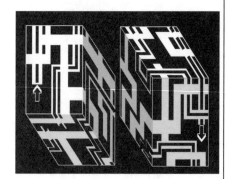

Maze 15

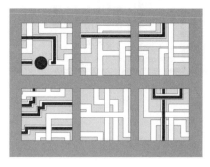

SOLUTIONS

Maze 16

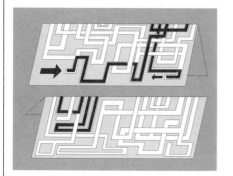

Maze 17

Maze 18

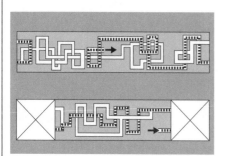

Maze 19

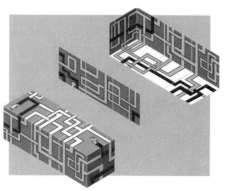

Maze 20

A-L-C-G-M-B-J-F-O-D-H-N-E-I-P

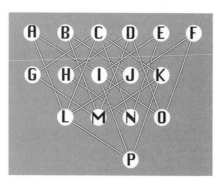

Maze 21

You're Logical

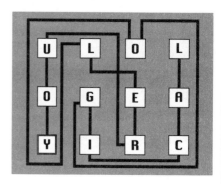

Maze 22

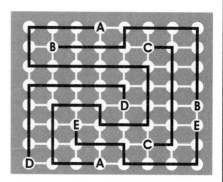

SOLUTIONS

Maze 23

Change the O to a D

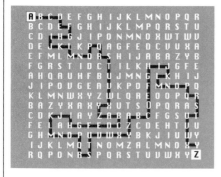

Maze 24

CAT, RAT, DOGS, TOP, NOSE, NOISE, LUNCH, HOT, SUPPER, ELBOW, JOINT, FIG, LOGIC, MAZE, BASEBALL, MITT, SAVE, ELEPHANT, ALLIGATOR, BAT, THAT , MOUSE.

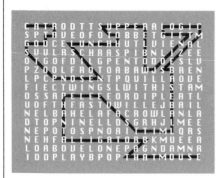

Maze 25

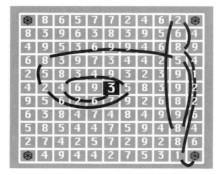

Maze 26

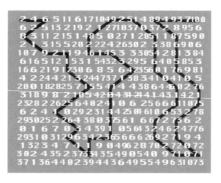

Maze 27

5-25-10-15-5-
25-10-5-OUT

Maze 28

3/4+1/4+3/4+
17/32+1/4+
3/4+1/4+
17/32+3/16=
5

Maze 29

1-6, 6-2, 2-5,
5-10, 10-9, 9-7,
7-4, 4-11, 11-8,
8-3, 3-12.

Maze 30

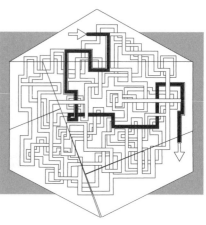

SOLUTIONS

Maze 33

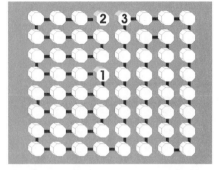

Maze 31

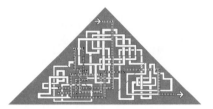

Maze 35

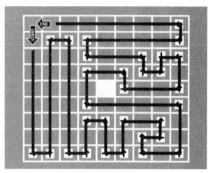

Maze 32

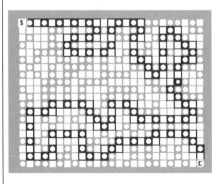

Maze 34

Maze 36

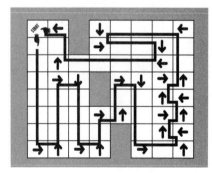

SOLUTIONS

Maze 37

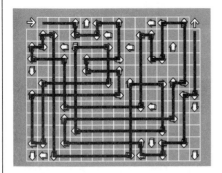

Maze 41

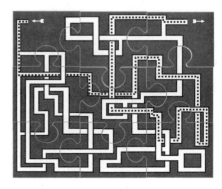

Maze 39

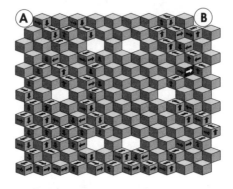

Maze 38

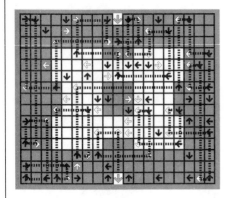

Maze 42

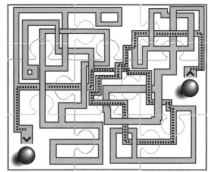

Maze 40

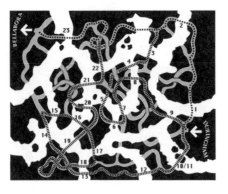

SOLUTIONS

Maze 43

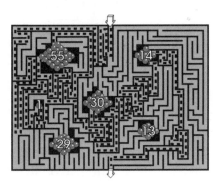

Maze 44

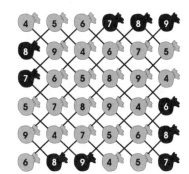

ABOUT THE AUTHOR

Larry Evans has been a resident of the Home For the Partially Bald for over 35 years. As an author and illustrator of over 25 books, he qualifies for sainthood in over twelve religions. He actually lives and works in his studio in San Francisco, California and goes outdoors when the weather's nice. If you disagree with any of the solutions in this book, Mr. Evans suggests that you create your own book and then see how well you take rejection.

INDEX

Abracadabra, 28
Almost Straight Down, 7
Alphabet Zoop, 29
Alphatrek, 26
Arrow Cubes, 48
Bad Arrow, The, 46
Barricades, The, 6
Black and White, 47
Boxed In, 19
Building Bridges, 50
Cannonballs, 53
Cat And Mouse, 30
Clear Logic, 18
Cube Root, 20
Down Side Up, 15

Ending Well, 44
Folding Fools, 21
Gone But Not Forgotten, 45
Hex or Square, 38
House of Mystery, The, 11
In the Beginning, 8
Ins and Outs, The, 5
Jigsaw Maze, 51
Jigsaw Too, 52
Möbius Madness, 23
Moneybags, 54
More Pinball Madness, 35
Number Fun, 32
Office Building, The, 12

One to Win, 10
Past Presidents, 36
Pinball Madness, 34
Pyramid, The, 22
Red Herring, The, 39
Round and Round, 42
Square Circles, 40
Three Cubes, 24
Three Nuts, 41
Under Construction, 16
Walls Only, 13
Warehouse, The, 14
Win Sum—Lose Sum, 33
You're Logical?, 27